To Laurel

With Hugs

Charlie Rose

With Love To My Daughter Alicia

For giving me the inspiration to
write this book and for giving me
little Ella to read it to.

LITTLE CHARLIE
AND HIS TU-TA-ROO BAND

By Charlie Prose

Verse by

Dorothy Rose Seiden

To learn more about Tu-Ta-Roos visit our website
www.charlieprose.com

One hundred percent of all profits from the sale of this book will be donated to The Helping Hands Society, 301 Rocky Road, Hazleton, PA 18201. Their mission is to provide comprehensive therapies and services for disabled children.

Special thanks to Dorothy Rose Seiden for transforming my story into beautiful rhyming verse, and for her desire to help all children by donating her work on this book. Without her generosity this book would not be possible.

published by charlie prose productions, po box 809, mays landing nj 08330
ISBN 978-0-615-17777-9

ILLUSTRATIONS BY: TD

this is a booksjustbooks book

"There is no greater challenge,
no greater gift and no greater reward
than to awaken the imagination of a child."

Charlie Prose

Charlie was a little boy
Who didn't have any toys.

No TV games or videos
Like all the other boys.

But Charlie never missed the things
His parents couldn't afford,
Because he had his TU-TA-ROO
And he was never bored.

8

'Twas just a cardboard tube on which
The paper towels were rolled,
But Charlie couldn't have loved it more
If it were made of gold.

9

The other kids looked down on him.
They teased him every day.

10

"That cardboard tube is not a toy.
We don't want you to play."

Yet Charlie was a happy boy,
A kind and loving son.
He always had his TU-TA-ROOS
To play with and have fun.

While Charlie played, the other kids
Just watched their toys and trains.
They pulled a switch and then sat back,
Didn't have to use their brains.

13

One day a strange event occurred,
There weren't any lights.

The batteries in toys wouldn't work.
It started many fights.

15

No television shows to watch.
Computers were dark, too.

No DVD's or CD songs,
"There's nothing left to do."

17

Along came Charlie down the street,
As happy as could be.
"I have some extra TU-TA-ROOS,
Won't you all play with me?"

18

He handed out the TU-TA-ROOS.
"It will be really grand.
If you each play an instrument,
Then we can have a band."

"Pretend one is a saxophone,
A bugle or bassoon."

20

"Harmonica or piccolo.
We'll play a lively tune."

"Trombone or tuba, flute or horn,
We nearly are all set."

23

"You – use the TU-TA-ROOS for sticks
To beat upon a drum."

24

"You – twirl one like a large baton.
The rest of you can hum."

25

The people ran outside to watch
The children all pretend.
That they were in a marching band
With Charlie, their new friend.

26

You do not need expensive things
In order to have fun,
Imagination is the key,
And each of you has one.

Be sure to use it everyday,
And you can be a star.
For you can do most anything,
No matter who you are.

Award-winning entertainer Charlie Prose has been making people laugh with his family friendly humor for over 40 years. His love for children and dedication to helping physically and mentally disabled children is one of his passions in life.

Marty Lerario, Martin Photography, Inc.